The Thinking Tree

BOOK OF
DANCE
HOMESCHOOLING
CURRICULUM JOURNAL

Study 40 Different Types
of Modern & Traditional Dance
From All Around the World

This Book Belongs to:

Mamac S. Bernard

DATE:

September 7, 2024

By: Sarah Janisse Brown
Illustrations By: Serge Andreev
Designed By: Margarita Brown

FunSchooling.com

DANCES COVERED IN THE BOOK:

TABLE OF CONTENTS:

About this Book:

This Book of Dance focuses on 40 different modern and traditional styles of dance from around the world. Creative students will research the culture, origins, music, traditions, costumes, and movements of each dance. The book is designed to appeal to both male and female students who enjoy dance and the arts. Leaning prompts will require the student to use the internet to learn more about each type of dance. It is important to have access to videos or documentaries that will help the student to watch the dance in action.

Students will have the opportunity to research and draw costumes associated with each dance and draw examples of the dance moves. Students who are not highly skilled in drawing may draw stick figures or comics! The book includes beautiful and accurate illustrations by Russian dancer and artist Serge Andreev. A student who loves dance will treasure every page and keep this journal as a portfolio of their passionate learning experience. This book is ideal for teens but can be used with younger students, with additional assistance.

Materials Needed:

Colored Pencils
Pencils
Gel Pens
Access to the internet for research
Books & documentaries about dance

RESEARCH MODERN & POPULAR DANCE AROUND THE WORLD

RESEARCH TRADITIONAL & CULTURAL DANCE AROUND THE WORLD

African Dance

Do some research and draw some moves from this style of dancing

Dance Study

African Dance

It's research time! Use the Internet, books, tutorials and documentaries to study this dance.

DESIGN A COSTUME FOR THIS TYPE OF DANCING

Where and when did this dance originate?

_____

_____

How was this dance invented? Tell the story:

_____
_____
_____
_____
_____
_____

What type of music and instruments commonly accompany
this type of dancing:

_____
_____
_____
_____
_____
_____
_____

What traditions or customs are associated with this
dance?

_____
_____
_____
_____
_____
_____
_____

Share three random facts about this dance:

1_____
_____

2_____
_____

3_____

American Native Dance

Do some research and draw some moves
from this style of dancing

Dance Study

American Native Dance

It's research time! Use the Internet, books, tutorials and documentaries to study this dance.

DESIGN A COSTUME FOR THIS TYPE OF DANCING

Where and when did this dance originate?

_____

_____

How was this dance invented? Tell the story:

_____

_____

_____

_____

_____

_____

_____

What type of music and instruments commonly accompany this type of dancing:

_____

_____

_____

_____

_____

_____

_____

_____

What traditions or customs are associated with this dance?

_____

_____

_____

_____

_____

_____

_____

Share three random facts about this dance:

1_____

_____

2_____

_____

3_____

Armenian Dance

Do some research and draw some moves from this style of dancing

Dance Study

Armenian Dance

It's research time! Use the Internet, books, tutorials and documentaries to study this dance.

DESIGN A COSTUME FOR THIS TYPE OF DANCING

Where and when did this dance originate?

_____

_____

How was this dance invented? Tell the story:

_____

_____

_____

_____

_____

_____

What type of music and instruments commonly accompany
this type of dancing:

_____

_____

_____

_____

_____

_____

_____

What traditions or customs are associated with this
dance?

_____

_____

_____

_____

_____

_____

_____

Share three random facts about this dance:

1_____

_____

2_____

_____

3_____

Ballet

Do some research and draw some moves from this style of dancing

Dance Study

Ballet

It's research time! Use the Internet, books, tutorials and documentaries to study this dance.

DESIGN A COSTUME FOR THIS TYPE OF DANCING

Where and when did this dance originate?

_____

_____

How was this dance invented? Tell the story:

_____

_____

_____

_____

_____

What type of music and instruments commonly accompany this type of dancing:

_____

_____

_____

_____

_____

_____

_____

What traditions or customs are associated with this dance?

_____

_____

_____

_____

_____

_____

_____

Share three random facts about this dance:

1_____

2_____

3_____

Break Dance

Do some research and draw some moves from this style of dancing

Dance Study

Break Dance

It's research time! Use the Internet, books, tutorials and documentaries to study this dance.

DESIGN A COSTUME FOR THIS TYPE OF DANCING

Where and when did this dance originate?

_____
_____

How was this dance invented? Tell the story:

_____
_____
_____
_____
_____
_____
_____

What type of music and instruments commonly accompany this type of dancing:

_____
_____
_____
_____
_____
_____
_____
_____

What traditions or customs are associated with this dance?

_____
_____
_____
_____
_____
_____
_____
_____

Share three random facts about this dance:

1_____

2_____

3_____

Buryat National Dance

Do some research and draw some moves from this style of dancing

Dance Study

Buryat National Dance

It's research time! Use the Internet, books, tutorials and documentaries to study this dance.

DESIGN A COSTUME FOR THIS TYPE OF DANCING

Where and when did this dance originate?

_____
_____

How was this dance invented? Tell the story:

_____
_____
_____
_____
_____
_____

What type of music and instruments commonly accompany this type of dancing:

_____
_____
_____
_____
_____
_____
_____

What traditions or customs are associated with this dance?

_____
_____
_____
_____
_____
_____
_____

Share three random facts about this dance:

1_____

2_____

3_____

Capoiera

Do some research and draw some moves from this style of dancing

Dance Study

Capoiera

It's research time! Use the Internet, books, tutorials and documentaries to study this dance.

DESIGN A COSTUME FOR THIS TYPE OF DANCING

Where and when did this dance originate?

_____

_____

How was this dance invented? Tell the story:

_____
_____
_____
_____
_____
_____
_____

What type of music and instruments commonly accompany this type of dancing:

_____
_____
_____
_____
_____
_____
_____
_____
_____

What traditions or customs are associated with this dance?

_____
_____
_____
_____
_____
_____
_____

Share three random facts about this dance:

1_____

2_____

3_____

Cha-cha-cha

Do some research and draw some moves
from this style of dancing

Dance Study

Cha-cha-cha

It's research time! Use the Internet, books, tutorials and documentaries to study this dance.

DESIGN A COSTUME FOR THIS TYPE OF DANCING

Where and when did this dance originate?

_____

_____

How was this dance invented? Tell the story:

_____

_____

_____

_____

_____

_____

What type of music and instruments commonly accompany this type of dancing:

_____

_____

_____

_____

_____

_____

_____

What traditions or customs are associated with this dance?

_____

_____

_____

_____

_____

_____

_____

Share three random facts about this dance:

1_____

2_____

3_____

Chukotka Dance

Do some research and draw some moves from this style of dancing

Dance Study

Chukotka Dance

It's research time! Use the Internet, books, tutorials and documentaries to study this dance.

DESIGN A COSTUME FOR THIS TYPE OF DANCING

Where and when did this dance originate?

_____

_____

How was this dance invented? Tell the story:

_____
_____
_____
_____
_____
_____

What type of music and instruments commonly accompany this type of dancing:

_____
_____
_____
_____
_____
_____
_____

What traditions or customs are associated with this dance?

_____
_____
_____
_____
_____
_____
_____

Share three random facts about this dance:

1_____

2_____

3_____

Contemporary Dance

Do some research and draw some moves from this style of dancing

Dance Study

Contemporary Dance

It's research time! Use the Internet, books, tutorials and documentaries to study this dance.

DESIGN A COSTUME FOR THIS TYPE OF DANCING

Where and when did this dance originate?

_____

_____

How was this dance invented? Tell the story:

_____

_____

_____

_____

_____

_____

What type of music and instruments commonly accompany this type of dancing:

_____

_____

_____

_____

_____

_____

_____

What traditions or customs are associated with this dance?

_____

_____

_____

_____

_____

_____

_____

Share three random facts about this dance:

1_____

2_____

3_____

Korean Traditional Dance (Jeongjae)

Do some research and draw some moves from this style of dancing

Dance Study

Korean Traditional Dance (Jeongjae)

It's research time! Use the Internet, books, tutorials and documentaries to study this dance.

DESIGN A COSTUME FOR THIS TYPE OF DANCING

Where and when did this dance originate?

_____

_____

How was this dance invented? Tell the story:

_____

_____

_____

_____

_____

_____

What type of music and instruments commonly accompany
this type of dancing:

_____

_____

_____

_____

_____

_____

_____

What traditions or customs are associated with this
dance?

_____

_____

_____

_____

_____

_____

Share three random facts about this dance:

1_____

2_____

3_____

Cowboy Dance

Do some research and draw some moves from this style of dancing

Dance Study

Cowboy Dance

It's research time! Use the Internet, books, tutorials and documentaries to study this dance.

DESIGN A COSTUME FOR THIS TYPE OF DANCING

Where and when did this dance originate?

_____

_____

How was this dance invented? Tell the story:

_____

_____

_____

_____

_____

_____

What type of music and instruments commonly accompany
this type of dancing:

_____

_____

_____

_____

_____

_____

_____

What traditions or customs are associated with this
dance?

_____

_____

_____

_____

_____

_____

_____

Share three random facts about this dance:

1_____

_____

2_____

_____

3_____

Crump

Do some research and draw some moves from this style of dancing

Dance Study

Crump

It's research time! Use the Internet, books, tutorials and documentaries to study this dance.

DESIGN A COSTUME FOR THIS TYPE OF DANCING

Where and when did this dance originate?

_____
_____

How was this dance invented? Tell the story:

_____
_____
_____
_____
_____
_____

What type of music and instruments commonly accompany this type of dancing:

_____
_____
_____
_____
_____
_____
_____

What traditions or customs are associated with this dance?

_____
_____
_____
_____
_____
_____

Share three random facts about this dance:

1_____
_____
2_____
_____
3_____

C-walk

Do some research and draw some moves from this style of dancing

Dance Study

It's research time! Use the Internet, books, tutorials and documentaries to study this dance.

DESIGN a COSTUME FOR tHIS tYPE OF DanCING

Where and when did this dance originate?

_____
_____

How was this dance invented? Tell the story:

_____
_____
_____
_____
_____
_____
_____

What type of music and instruments commonly accompany this type of dancing:

_____
_____
_____
_____
_____
_____
_____
_____
_____

What traditions or customs are associated with this dance?

_____
_____
_____
_____
_____
_____
_____

Share three random facts about this dance:

1_____
_____
2_____
_____
3_____

Dervish Dance (Turkish)

Do some research and draw some moves from this style of dancing

Dance Study

Dervish Ddance (Turkish)

It's research time! Use the Internet, books, tutorials and documentaries to study this dance.

DESIGN A COSTUME FOR THIS TYPE OF DANCING

Where and when did this dance originate?

_____

_____

How was this dance invented? Tell the story:

_____

_____

_____

_____

_____

_____

What type of music and instruments commonly accompany this type of dancing:

_____

_____

_____

_____

_____

_____

_____

What traditions or customs are associated with this dance?

_____

_____

_____

_____

_____

_____

_____

Share three random facts about this dance:

1_____

2_____

3_____

Electro Dance

Do some research and draw some moves from this style of dancing

Dance Study

Electro Dance

It's research time! Use the Internet, books, tutorials and documentaries to study this dance.

DESIGN A COSTUME FOR THIS TYPE OF DANCING

Where and when did this dance originate?

_____

_____

How was this dance invented? Tell the story:

_____

_____

_____

_____

_____

_____

What type of music and instruments commonly accompany this type of dancing:

_____

_____

_____

_____

_____

_____

_____

_____

What traditions or customs are associated with this dance?

_____

_____

_____

_____

_____

_____

_____

Share three random facts about this dance:

1_____

_____

2_____

_____

3_____

Flamenco Dance

Do some research and draw some moves from this style of dancing

Dance Study

Flamenco

It's research time! Use the Internet, books, tutorials and documentaries to study this dance.

DESIGN A COSTUME FOR THIS TYPE OF DANCING

Where and when did this dance originate?

_____

_____

How was this dance invented? Tell the story:

_____

_____

_____

_____

_____

_____

What type of music and instruments commonly accompany this type of dancing:

_____

_____

_____

_____

_____

_____

_____

_____

What traditions or customs are associated with this dance?

_____

_____

_____

_____

_____

_____

_____

Share three random facts about this dance:

1_____

2_____

3_____

Georgian Dance

Do some research and draw some moves from this style of dancing

Dance Study

Georgian Dance

It's research time! Use the Internet, books, tutorials and documentaries to study this dance.

DESIGN A COSTUME FOR THIS TYPE OF DANCING

Where and when did this dance originate?

_____

_____

How was this dance invented? Tell the story:

_____

_____

_____

_____

_____

_____

What type of music and instruments commonly accompany this type of dancing:

_____

_____

_____

_____

_____

_____

_____

What traditions or customs are associated with this dance?

_____

_____

_____

_____

_____

_____

Share three random facts about this dance:

1_____

_____

2_____

_____

3_____

Hebrew Dance

Do some research and draw some moves from this style of dancing

Dance Study

Hebrew Dance

It's research time! Use the Internet, books, tutorials and documentaries to study this dance.

DESIGN A COSTUME FOR THIS TYPE OF DANCING

Where and when did this dance originate?

_____

_____

How was this dance invented? Tell the story:

_____

_____

_____

_____

_____

_____

_____

What type of music and instruments commonly accompany
this type of dancing:

_____

_____

_____

_____

_____

_____

_____

_____

What traditions or customs are associated with this
dance?

_____

_____

_____

_____

_____

_____

_____

Share three random facts about this dance:

1_____

_____

2_____

_____

3_____

Hip-Hop

Do some research and draw some moves from this style of dancing

Dance Study

Hip-Hop

It's research time! Use the Internet, books, tutorials and documentaries to study this dance.

DESIGN A COSTUME FOR THIS TYPE OF DANCING

Where and when did this dance originate?

_____

_____

How was this dance invented? Tell the story:

_____

_____

_____

_____

_____

_____

What type of music and instruments commonly accompany this type of dancing:

_____

_____

_____

_____

_____

_____

_____

What traditions or customs are associated with this dance?

_____

_____

_____

_____

_____

_____

Share three random facts about this dance:

1_____

_____

2_____

_____

3_____

Indian Classical Dance

Do some research and draw some moves from this style of dancing

Dance Study

Indian Classical Dance

It's research time! Use the Internet, books, tutorials and documentaries to study this dance.

DESIGN A COSTUME FOR THIS TYPE OF DANCING

Where and when did this dance originate?

_____
_____

How was this dance invented? Tell the story:

_____
_____
_____
_____
_____
_____
_____

What type of music and instruments commonly accompany this type of dancing:

_____
_____
_____
_____
_____
_____
_____
_____
_____

What traditions or customs are associated with this dance?

_____
_____
_____
_____
_____
_____
_____
_____

Share three random facts about this dance:

1_____
_____
2_____
_____
3_____

Irish Dance

Do some research and draw some moves
from this style of dancing

Dance Study

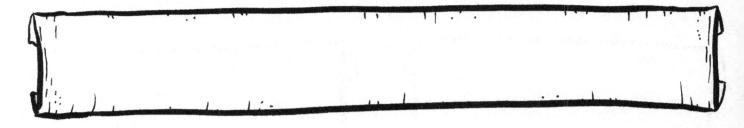

It's research time! Use the Internet, books, tutorials and documentaries to study this dance.

DESIGN A COSTUME FOR THIS TYPE OF DANCING

Where and when did this dance originate?

_____

_____

How was this dance invented? Tell the story:

_____

_____

_____

_____

_____

_____

What type of music and instruments commonly accompany this type of dancing:

_____

_____

_____

_____

_____

_____

_____

What traditions or customs are associated with this dance?

_____

_____

_____

_____

_____

_____

Share three random facts about this dance:

1_____

_____

2_____

_____

3_____

Japanese Traditional Dance

Do some research and draw some moves from this style of dancing

Dance Study

Japanese Traditional Dance

It's research time! Use the Internet, books, tutorials and documentaries to study this dance.

DESIGN A COSTUME FOR THIS TYPE OF DANCING

Where and when did this dance originate?

_____

_____

How was this dance invented? Tell the story:

_____

_____

_____

_____

_____

_____

What type of music and instruments commonly accompany
this type of dancing:

_____

_____

_____

_____

_____

_____

_____

What traditions or customs are associated with this
dance?

_____

_____

_____

_____

_____

_____

Share three random facts about this dance:

1_____

2_____

3_____

Jazz-Funk

Do some research and draw some moves from this style of dancing

Dance Study

Jazz-Funk

It's research time! Use the Internet, books, tutorials and documentaries to study this dance.

DESIGN A COSTUME FOR THIS TYPE OF DANCING

Where and when did this dance originate?

_____
_____

How was this dance invented? Tell the story:

_____
_____
_____
_____
_____
_____

What type of music and instruments commonly accompany this type of dancing:

_____
_____
_____
_____
_____
_____
_____
_____

What traditions or customs are associated with this dance?

_____
_____
_____
_____
_____
_____
_____

Share three random facts about this dance:

1_____

2_____

3_____

Contemporary Jazz Dance

Do some research and draw some moves from this style of dancing

Dance Study

Contemporary Jazz Dance

It's research time! Use the Internet, books, tutorials and documentaries to study this dance.

DESIGN A COSTUME FOR THIS TYPE OF DANCING

Where and when did this dance originate?

_____

_____

How was this dance invented? Tell the story:

_____

_____

_____

_____

_____

_____

What type of music and instruments commonly accompany this type of dancing:

_____

_____

_____

_____

_____

_____

_____

What traditions or customs are associated with this dance?

_____

_____

_____

_____

_____

_____

Share three random facts about this dance:

1 _____

2 _____

3 _____

Moldavian Dance

Do some research and draw some moves from this style of dancing

Dance Study

Moldavian Dance

It's research time! Use the Internet, books, tutorials and documentaries to study this dance.

DESIGN A COSTUME FOR THIS TYPE OF DANCING

Where and when did this dance originate?

_____

_____

How was this dance invented? Tell the story:

_____

_____

_____

_____

_____

_____

What type of music and instruments commonly accompany this type of dancing:

_____

_____

_____

_____

_____

_____

_____

_____

What traditions or customs are associated with this dance?

_____

_____

_____

_____

_____

_____

_____

Share three random facts about this dance:

1_____

_____

2_____

_____

3_____

J-funk

Do some research and draw some moves from this style of dancing

Dance Study

It's research time! Use the Internet, books, tutorials and documentaries to study this dance.

DESIGN A COSTUME FOR THIS TYPE OF DANCING

Where and when did this dance originate?

_____

_____

How was this dance invented? Tell the story:

_____

_____

_____

_____

_____

_____

What type of music and instruments commonly accompany this type of dancing:

_____

_____

_____

_____

_____

_____

_____

What traditions or customs are associated with this dance?

_____

_____

_____

_____

_____

_____

Share three random facts about this dance:

1_____

2_____

3_____

Popping

Do some research and draw some moves from this style of dancing

Dance Study

Popping

It's research time! Use the Internet, books, tutorials and documentaries to study this dance.

DESIGN A COSTUME FOR THIS TYPE OF DANCING

Where and when did this dance originate?

_____

_____

How was this dance invented? Tell the story:

_____

_____

_____

_____

_____

_____

What type of music and instruments commonly accompany
this type of dancing:

_____

_____

_____

_____

_____

_____

_____

_____

What traditions or customs are associated with this
dance?

_____

_____

_____

_____

_____

_____

_____

Share three random facts about this dance:

1_____

_____

2_____

_____

3_____

Quickstep (Foxtrot)

Do some research and draw some moves from this style of dancing

Dance Study

Quickstep (Foxtrot)

It's research time! Use the Internet, books, tutorials and documentaries to study this dance.

DESIGN A COSTUME FOR THIS TYPE OF DANCING

Where and when did this dance originate?

_____

_____

How was this dance invented? Tell the story:

_____

_____

_____

_____

_____

_____

What type of music and instruments commonly accompany this type of dancing:

_____

_____

_____

_____

_____

_____

_____

What traditions or customs are associated with this dance?

_____

_____

_____

_____

_____

_____

Share three random facts about this dance:

1_____

2_____

3_____

R&B

Do some research and draw some moves from this style of dancing

Dance Study

R&B

It's research time! Use the Internet, books, tutorials and documentaries to study this dance.

DESIGN A COSTUME FOR THIS TYPE OF DANCING

Where and when did this dance originate?

_____
_____

How was this dance invented? Tell the story:

_____
_____
_____
_____
_____
_____

What type of music and instruments commonly accompany this type of dancing:

_____
_____
_____
_____
_____
_____
_____

What traditions or customs are associated with this dance?

_____
_____
_____
_____
_____
_____

Share three random facts about this dance:

1_____

2_____

3_____

Romani Dance

Do some research and draw some moves from this style of dancing

Dance Study

Romani Dance

It's research time! Use the Internet, books, tutorials and documentaries to study this dance.

DESIGN A COSTUME FOR THIS TYPE OF DANCING

Where and when did this dance originate?

_____

_____

How was this dance invented? Tell the story:

_____

_____

_____

_____

_____

_____

What type of music and instruments commonly accompany
this type of dancing:

_____

_____

_____

_____

_____

_____

_____

_____

What traditions or customs are associated with this
dance?

_____

_____

_____

_____

_____

_____

_____

_____

Share three random facts about this dance:

1_____

2_____

3_____

Russian Folk Dance

Do some research and draw some moves from this style of dancing

Dance Study

Russian Folk Dance

It's research time! Use the Internet, books, tutorials and documentaries to study this dance.

DESIGN A COSTUME FOR THIS TYPE OF DANCING

Where and when did this dance originate?

_____

_____

How was this dance invented? Tell the story:

_____

_____

_____

_____

_____

_____

What type of music and instruments commonly accompany
this type of dancing:

_____

_____

_____

_____

_____

_____

_____

_____

What traditions or customs are associated with this
dance?

_____

_____

_____

_____

_____

_____

_____

Share three random facts about this dance:

1_____

_____

2_____

_____

3_____

Scottish Folk Dance

Do some research and draw some moves
from this style of dancing

Dance Study

Scottish Folk Dance

It's research time! Use the Internet, books, tutorials and documentaries to study this dance.

DESIGN A COSTUME FOR THIS TYPE OF DANCING

Where and when did this dance originate?

_____
_____

How was this dance invented? Tell the story:

_____
_____
_____
_____
_____
_____

What type of music and instruments commonly accompany this type of dancing:

_____
_____
_____
_____
_____
_____
_____

What traditions or customs are associated with this dance?

_____
_____
_____
_____
_____
_____

Share three random facts about this dance:

1_____
_____
2_____
_____
3_____

Shuffle Dance

Do some research and draw some moves from this style of dancing

Dance Study

Shuffle Dance

It's research time! Use the Internet, books, tutorials and documentaries to study this dance.

DESIGN A COSTUME FOR THIS TYPE OF DANCING

Where and when did this dance originate?

_____
_____

How was this dance invented? Tell the story:

_____
_____
_____
_____
_____
_____
_____

What type of music and instruments commonly accompany this type of dancing:

_____
_____
_____
_____
_____
_____
_____
_____
_____

What traditions or customs are associated with this dance?

_____
_____
_____
_____
_____
_____
_____
_____

Share three random facts about this dance:

1_____
_____
2_____
_____
3_____

Step Dance

Do some research and draw some moves from this style of dancing

Dance Study

Step Dance

It's research time! Use the Internet, books, tutorials and documentaries to study this dance.

DESIGN A COSTUME FOR THIS TYPE OF DANCING

Where and when did this dance originate?

_____

_____

How was this dance invented? Tell the story:

_____

_____

_____

_____

_____

_____

What type of music and instruments commonly accompany
this type of dancing:

_____

_____

_____

_____

_____

_____

_____

What traditions or customs are associated with this
dance?

_____

_____

_____

_____

_____

_____

_____

Share three random facts about this dance:

1_____

2_____

3_____

Tectonic

Do some research and draw some moves from this style of dancing

Dance Study

Tectonic

It's research time! Use the Internet, books, tutorials and documentaries to study this dance.

DESIGN A COSTUME FOR THIS TYPE OF DANCING

Where and when did this dance originate?

_____

_____

How was this dance invented? Tell the story:

_____

_____

_____

_____

_____

_____

_____

What type of music and instruments commonly accompany
this type of dancing:

_____

_____

_____

_____

_____

_____

_____

_____

What traditions or customs are associated with this
dance?

_____

_____

_____

_____

_____

_____

_____

_____

Share three random facts about this dance:

1_____

_____

2_____

_____

3_____

Traditional Kazakh Dance

Do some research and draw some moves from this style of dancing

Dance Study

Traditional Kazakh Dance

It's research time! Use the Internet, books, tutorials and documentaries to study this dance.

DESIGN a COSTUME FOR tHiS tYPE OF DanCinG

Where and when did this dance originate?

_____

_____

How was this dance invented? Tell the story:

_____

_____

_____

_____

_____

_____

_____

What type of music and instruments commonly accompany this type of dancing:

_____

_____

_____

_____

_____

_____

_____

_____

What traditions or customs are associated with this dance?

_____

_____

_____

_____

_____

_____

_____

_____

Share three random facts about this dance:

1_____

_____

2_____

_____

3_____

Ukrainian Folk Dance- Hopak

Do some research and draw some moves from this style of dancing

Dance Study

Ukrainian Folk Dance- Hopak

It's research time! Use the Internet, books, tutorials and documentaries to study this dance.

DESIGN a COSTUME FOR THIS TYPE OF DANCING

Where and when did this dance originate?

_____
_____

How was this dance invented? Tell the story:

_____
_____
_____
_____
_____
_____
_____

What type of music and instruments commonly accompany this type of dancing:

_____
_____
_____
_____
_____
_____
_____
_____

What traditions or customs are associated with this dance?

_____
_____
_____
_____
_____
_____
_____

Share three random facts about this dance:

1_____

2_____

3_____

Uzbek Folk Dance

Do some research and draw some moves from this style of dancing

Dance Study

Uzbek Folk Dance

It's research time! Use the Internet, books, tutorials and documentaries to study this dance.

DESIGN A COSTUME FOR THIS TYPE OF DANCING

Where and when did this dance originate?

_____

_____

How was this dance invented? Tell the story:

_____

_____

_____

_____

_____

_____

What type of music and instruments commonly accompany
this type of dancing:

_____

_____

_____

_____

_____

_____

_____

What traditions or customs are associated with this
dance?

_____

_____

_____

_____

_____

_____

_____

Share three random facts about this dance:

1_____

_____

2_____

_____

3_____

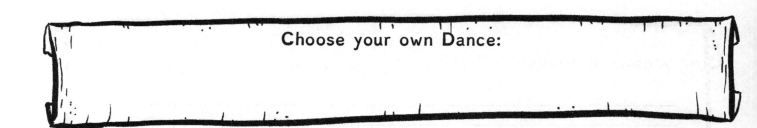

Choose your own Dance:

Do some research and draw some moves
from this style of dancing

Dance Study

Choose your own Dance:

German   Polka

It's research time! Use the Internet, books,
tutorials and documentaries to study this dance.

DESIGN A COSTUME FOR THIS TYPE OF DANCING

Where and when did this dance originate?

It began in the early 1800 hundreds in rural Germany empire.

How was this dance invented? Tell the story:

A young womens music teacher noticed that she was dancing uniquely to an upbeat tune. And from there it started expanding to different regions.

What type of music and instruments commonly accompany this type of dancing:

Brass, string, aerophone, wind, and percussion instruments.

What traditions or customs are associated with this dance?

The tradtional Lenderhosend and drindle outfits.

Share three random facts about this dance:

1 It spread quickly by peasants.

2 Reganded popularity after World War II.

3 Polka is popular in Wiscosin where the "Beer Barrel Polka" for halftime for the milwaukee Bucks games.

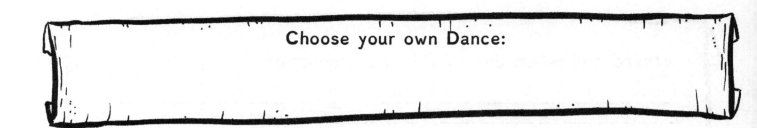

Choose your own Dance:

Do some research and draw some moves from this style of dancing

Dance Study

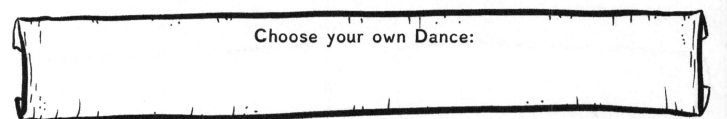

Choose your own Dance:

It's research time! Use the Internet, books, tutorials and documentaries to study this dance.

DESIGN A COSTUME FOR THIS TYPE OF DANCING

Where and when did this dance originate?

_____

_____

How was this dance invented? Tell the story:

_____

_____

_____

_____

_____

_____

What type of music and instruments commonly accompany this type of dancing:

_____

_____

_____

_____

_____

_____

_____

What traditions or customs are associated with this dance?

_____

_____

_____

_____

_____

_____

_____

Share three random facts about this dance:

1_____

2_____

3_____

Made in the USA
Monee, IL
05 August 2021